Tess and Paddy

Story by Joy Cowley

Tess is our neighbor's baby.
She is nearly two.

One weekend,
she came to stay with us.
She liked me.
She liked Mom and Dad.
Most of all,
she liked our dog Paddy.

3

Tess hugged Paddy
and pulled his tail.
When she got on his back,
he ran away, and Tess fell off.

"Bad dog!" she cried.

Tess didn't like her dinner,
so she gave it to Paddy.
He didn't like it either.

Then Tess went to Paddy's dish
and tried to eat Paddy's dinner.

Paddy growled at her.

Tess growled back.
"Bad dog!" she said.

8

Mom came in and grabbed Tess.
"Don't let her eat Paddy's food!"
Mom yelled at me.

"Why not?" I said.
"We can get Paddy some more."

"It's not good for Tess!"
Mom yelled.

All that yelling
was too much for Paddy and Tess.
Paddy went under the table.
Tess cried.

After dinner,
Paddy and Tess became friends.
Paddy splashed in Tess's pool.
Tess splashed in Paddy's bowl.

Tess slept in Paddy's bed.
Paddy slept in Tess's bed.

The next morning, Tess got dressed.
She also dressed Paddy.
She put a scarf
and some socks on him.

Paddy chewed holes in the scarf.

"That was a new scarf!"
cried Mom.

When it was time to go,
Tess hugged Paddy
and Paddy licked Tess.

"Good dog," said Tess.

"Was Tess all right?"
asked her mother.

15

"No trouble," said Mom.
"It was like having
two dogs in the house."